To ~~Hannah~~ T. Racey 1991

With Love,
From
GRANDMA + GRMNPA

Jesus Loves You, Too!

"FROM A CHILD THOU HAST KNOWN THE HOLY SCRIPTURES"

"All thy children shall be taught of the Lord: and great shall be the peace of thy children" (Isaiah 54:13).

The
Bible-Time
Nursery Rhyme Book

By Emily Hunter

With Illustrations by the Author

MANNA PUBLICATIONS
Box 1111, Camas, WA 98607

1st Printing, 1981 - 15,575
2nd Printing, 1981 - 30,670
3rd Printing, 1983 - 51,656
4th Printing, 1984 - 75,000

ISBN 0-939744-04-X

Printed in the United States of America

THE FIRST MAN AND WOMAN

God made Adam from the ground,
And gave him breath of life.
God made Eve from Adam's rib,
And she became his wife.

"And the Lord God formed man of the dust of the ground and breathed into his nostrils the breath of life" (Gen. 2:7).

GOD MADE EACH OF US

God made Adam and Eve, 'tis true.
   He also made me. He also made you.
He made each father. He made each mother.
   He made each sister. He made each brother.
   And none of us is like the other.

      Look around, and you will see
        That no one else is just like me,
      But we all live together in a happy family!

"He giveth to all life, and breath" (Acts 17:25).

ADAM NAMED THE ANIMALS

"And whatsoever Adam called every living creature, that was the name thereof" (Gen. 2:19).

Adam gave the animals
  Every one a name.
Here are some for you to guess—
  A happy "naming game"!

I'm gentle, mild...I nibble grass.
  My wooly coat grows deep.
Adam took one look at me
  And said, "I name you —————."
                          (Sheep)

My tail is curly...nose, a snout.
  I'm smooth and round and big.
Adam took one look at me,
  And said, "I name you —————."
                        (Pig)

I'm big, with heavy paws and claws.
  I'm covered with brown hair.
Adam took one look at me,
  And said, "I name you —————."
                    (Bear)

I'm noble, handsome, sleek and strong.
  I run with speed and force.
Adam took one look at me,
  And said, "I name you —————."
                    (Horse)

I swing and leap from tree to tree.
My chattering is spunky.
Adam took one look at me,
And said, "I name you ————————."
(Monkey)

I climb high rocks and mountain cliffs.
I wear a white fur coat.
Adam took one look and said,
"Your name is Mountain ——————."
(Goat)

Lettuce leaves and carrot tops
Could be my daily habit.
Adam took one look at me,
And said, "I name you ——————."
(Rabbit)

My neck's so very, very long
That I made Adam laugh.
And then he said, "I think your name
Should surely be ——————."
(Giraffe)

My tail is ringed, my face is masked.
I'm seldom seen at noon.
Adam took one look at me,
And said, "Your name's ————————."
(Raccoon)

I AM ME
AND
YOU ARE YOU

I am me, and you are you.

I don't stand or walk like you.

I don't smile or talk like you,

For God made one of me—not two!

I am me, and you are you.

I don't sing a song like you,

Or even hum along like you,

For God made one of me—not two!

I am me, and you are you.

I don't run and skip like you,

And I don't hoppety-hip like you,

For God made one of me—not two!

I am me, and you are you.

I don't drink or eat like you,

Or even chew my meat like you,

For God made one of me—not two!

I am me, and you are you.

I don't write or draw like you,

And I don't color at all like you,

For God made one of me—not two!

I am me, and you are you.

I don't sleep in bed like you,

Or even lay my head like you,

For I am me, and you are you.

God made one of me—not two!

"For who maketh thee to differ from another (I Cor. 4:7)?

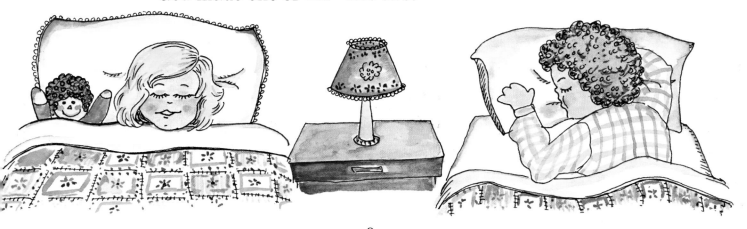

9

GOD GAVE ME A BODY HOUSE

"I am wonderfully made" (Ps. 139:14).

God gave me a body house.
  It's mine to keep and prize.
I look out from my body house
  Through my two window eyes.

My window eyes have eyelids.
  They are my window shades.
My eyelids I can lower.
  My eyelids I can raise.

Each time I lie down for my nap,
  My window shades come down.

But when I raise them up again,
  The light is all around.

I thank you, God, for window eyes,
  Because they help me see
The whole wide world and everything
  That is outside of me.

My body house has hearing ears
  On each side of my head.
Without my ears I'd never hear
  A word that's being said.

Without my ears, I'd never hear
  My own voice when I speak.
I wouldn't even hear a mouse
  When it goes "squeak-squeak-squeak"!

SQUEAK!

My body house has lips that speak,
  That laugh or smile or cry.
My lips can say "hello" to you.
  My lips can say "goodbye."

I thank you, God, for lips that speak.
  Please help me not to say
Cross words that make another sad,
  But happy words each day!

"My lips shall praise thee"
(Ps. 63:3).

"The hearing ear, and the seeing eye, the Lord hath made even both of them" (Prov. 20:12).

11

MR. MOON

Mr. Moon, up in the sky,
 Why are you there?
  Tell me why!

God placed me here
 With the stars so bright
To shine for you
 The long, dark night.

*"And God made two great lights;
the greater light to rule the day,
and the lesser light
to rule the night:
he made the stars also"*
(Gen. 1:16).

MR. SUN

Mr. Sun, up in the sky,
 Why are you there?
  Tell me why!

God placed me here
 To shine all day,
To give you light
 As you work and play.

12

GOD GAVE US COLORS

"He hath made everything beautiful" (Eccl. 3:11).

God gave us blue
In the sky up above.

God gave us red
In the apples we love.

God gave us orange
In pumpkins for pie.

God gave us purple
In grapes hanging high.

God gave us yellow
In the lemons we eat.

God gave us green
In the grass at our feet.

I am so glad we have colors so bright.
God could have made our world all black and white!

GOD MADE ALL CREATURES
TO BE THE WAY THEY ARE

"I am wonderfully made" (Ps. 139:14).

Worm, worm! Squiggly worm!.
Why do you wriggle and squiggle and squirm?
  Why do I wriggle and squiggle
    and squirm?
  Because God made me
    a squiggly worm!

      Fish, fish! Swishing fish!
       Why do you swim through the water a-swish?
       Why do I swim through the
         water a-swish?
         Because God made me
          a swishing fish!

Butterfly, butterfly in the sky!
Why do your wings go fluttering by?
  Why do I
    flutter by
      in the sky?
Because God made me a butterfly!

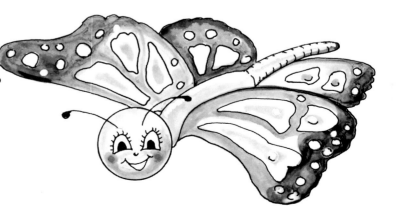

WHERE DID ADAM AND EVE LIVE?

"And the Lord God planted a garden...and there he put the man" (Gen. 2:8).

Where did Adam and Eve live,
   Alone in the world so new?
They lived in a beautiful garden spot
   Where trees and flowers grew.

And Adam and Eve were happy there,
   This very first man and wife.
They knew no worry, they knew no care,
   For God had given them life.

And all the fruit of the garden was theirs,
   The plums and cherries sweet,
Excepting the fruit of a certain tree
   God told them never to eat.

He said, "Don't eat the fruit of that tree."
   And then He told them why.
"Because," He said, "if you eat of that tree,
   Then you will surely die!"

"Of the tree of the knowledge of good and evil thou shalt not eat...In the day thou eatest thereof, thou shalt surely die" (Gen. 2:17).

THE SNAKE THAT TALKED

One day when Eve
    went out for a walk,
What did she meet,
    but a snake that could talk!

Hiding behind the forbidden tree,
    The snake spoke to her
      as plain as could be.

"Eve," he smiled, "God told you a lie!
    Eating this fruit will not make you die!"
So Eve ate the fruit, and Adam did too...
    Exactly what God told them not to do!

Later when God called to Adam, "Come here!"
They both ran and hid in shame and in fear.
    No longer happy or unafraid,
They now were sorry they'd disobeyed.

And just as God said, one day they died,
    For God's Word was true...
      'twas the snake who lied.

But God loved them so,
    that He made a way
So both could live in Heaven one day.

*"She took of the fruit, and did eat,
and gave also to her husband;
and he did eat" (Gen. 3:6).*

16

A GARDEN OF WEEDS

Glad, glad Adam who lived long ago
  Had the first garden that ever did grow.
Peas and lettuce one day he found
  Pushing their way up out of the ground.

Then one day—a surprise indeed!
  Adam looked down at the very first weed.
Adam knew he had done a bad deed,
  So now sad Adam had a garden to weed.

Glad, glad Adam was sad Adam now!
  Working all day by the sweat of his brow!
For every time Adam sowed ten seeds,
  He looked and found there were ten more weeds!

*"Because thou hast
eaten of the tree,
cursed is the ground...
thorns and thistles shall it bring forth"*
(Gen. 3:17, 18).

GOD MADE THE WATER

God made the water
   For the rivers and the lake.
God made the water
   For the baths that I take.

   God made the water
      For the oceans and the sea.
   God made the water
      For my grandma's cup of tea!

"God giveth rain upon the earth, and sendeth waters upon the fields" (Job 5:10).

THE FIRST BABY

"And Adam knew Eve his wife; and she bare Cain, and said, I have gotten a man from the LORD"
(Gen. 4:1).

The lambs and the deer
And the bunny all gazed,
And every little animal
Was very much amazed.

Something new and wonderful
Had happened on the earth.
Adam's wife, Eve, last night gave birth
To a tiny little baby—yes, a tiny baby boy.
Adam and his wife were filled with joy.

The birds flew by
Singing, "Tweet, tweet, tweet!
God's sent them a baby,
And isn't he sweet!"

19

THE OLDEST MAN EVER

"And all the days of Methuselah were nine hundred sixty and nine years" (Gen. 5:27).

If Methuselah had
    a birthday cake,
How many candles
    would it take?

'Twould take nine hundred
    and sixty-nine,
For Methuselah lived
    a LONG...
        LONG...
           TIME!

God Sees Me

"Thou God seest me"
(Gen. 16:13).

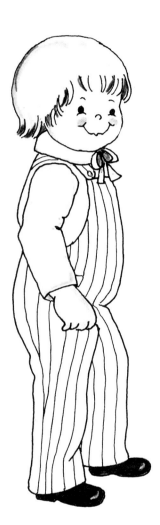

God sees me
    when I smile.
God sees me
    when I frown.
God sees me
    standing up.
God sees me
    sitting down.

God sees me
    in my bed.
God sees me
    take a walk.
He knows the words
    I'm going to say
Before I start
    to talk!

Noah's Ark

God said, "Noah,
There'll come a day,
When a flood will wash
Every creature away!

"So build an ark
Like a big, big boat,
And seal it well
So it will float."

So Noah followed
God's command,
And built an ark
Upon dry land.

He filled it up
Like a big, big zoo
With animals entering
Two
by
two.

In went the ducks
With a "quack,
quack, quack!"
In went the camels
With a hump on their back.

Came the giraffes
With necks held high,
While donkeys and horses
Came trotting by.

And through the door
  A hoot owl flew,
And when he saw Noah,
  He said, "Hoo...Hooo!"

"Baaa" went the sheep,
  And the cows went "moo..oo,"
While the rooster crowed,
  "A-cock-a-doodle-doo"!

Pigs and elephants,
  Birds and bears...
They all went into
  The ark in pairs.

When all were in,
　God shut the door.
And soon came the rain.
　It began to pour.

It rained and rained
　Till it covered the ground,
And soon not a house
　Or a tree could be found.

The waters covered
　The mountains high,
Until there was nothing
　But sea and sky.

But the animals and Noah
　Were safely afloat
On a big, big sea
　In a big, big, boat.

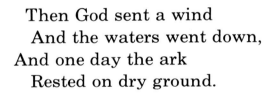

Then God sent a wind
　And the waters went down,
And one day the ark
　Rested on dry ground.

Out walked Noah
　And his family, too,
To live on the earth,
　Washed clean and new.

Out came the animals
　Short and tall,
And Noah thanked God
　For saving them all!

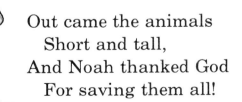

GOD KNOWS
YOUR NAME

God knows Jim,
And God knows Kim!

God knows Jane,
And God knows Wayne!

God knows Randy,
And God knows Sandy!

God knows Molly,
And God knows Polly!

God knows Sue,
And He knows TRACE 9 CRUM, too!
(Your name)

"I know thee by name"
(Ex. 33:17).

25

RAINBOW, RAINBOW!

"The bow shall be seen in the cloud:
and I will remember my promise...and the waters
shall no more become a flood" (Gen. 9:14, 15).

Rainbow, rainbow, high up in the sky!
Why are you up there? Can you tell us why?

God placed me here
In the heaven high above,
So you would remember
His promise of love...

To never again
Let the waters overflow
As they did in Noah's day
Long, long ago...

When they covered every mountain
And covered every tree,
So be happy...little children!
Every time you look at me!

26

THE SPARROWS

"Before you tuck us into bed,
　　Read us a story!" the sparrows pled.

So Mama read from the Holy Word,
　　"God cares for every little bird.

"God sees the tiny sparrow fall,
　　And watches o'er us one and all!"

THE TOWER OF BABEL

"Let us build us a city and a tower, whose top may reach unto heaven; and let us make us a name" (Gen. 11:4).

"Come!" said the men,
  "Let's make ourselves a name!
Let's build ourselves a tower,
  And get ourselves some fame!

"Let's all work together
  And make the tower high,
So it stretches up to heaven
  And reaches to the sky!"

But God above was watching
  As the men worked on the tower.
He saw they wanted greatness.
  He saw they wanted power.

He wasn't pleased with what he saw.
  He knew it wasn't good.
He said, "I'll mix their language
  So they can't be understood!"

So when a workman tried to talk
  With other workmen near,
Funny words and babble sounds
  Came drifting to his ear.

"Tee...lee! A-lah-doo-ween!"
  "What is that? What do you mean?"
"Pim-pam! A-dack-a-too!"
  "Well, I give up! I can't work with you!"

No longer could they talk,
  And no longer could they build.
They couldn't work together,
  So their hammers soon were stilled.

They couldn't live together,
  So they scattered far apart,
And that's how the languages
  First got their start.

28

LOVE ONE ANOTHER

The Bible says,
   Love one another.
Love your sister,
   Love your brother.

Love your father,
   Love your mother.
The Bible says,
   Love one another!

"This is my commandment, That ye love one another" (Jn 15:12).

THE LADDER TO HEAVEN

Sleepy Jacob
  looked around,
Looked around
  until he found
A great big stone
  upon the ground;
Put the stone
  beneath his head,
And that's the way
  he went to bed.

Jacob dreamed
  a dream that night...
Dreamed that night
  of angels bright,
Angels going
  up and down...
Down from heaven
  to the ground.

Up and down
  a ladder high...
High up to
  the starry sky,
And up above
  the angel's stair,
God Himself
  was standing there!

"He took of the stones and put them for his pillow, and lay down to sleep. And he dreamed, and behold a ladder set up on the earth, and the top of it reached to heaven. And behold the angels of God ascending and descending on it. And the Lord stood above it" (Gen. 28:11-13).

30

JOSEPH IN THE BOTTOM
OF THE PIT

Joseph, Joseph! Why do you sit
    There all alone in the bottom of the pit?
Why do I sit all alone in the pit?
    My brothers had a jealous fit,
And threw me here into this pit,
    So here in this pit, I sit and sit!

Where is your coat of red and blue,
    Purple, yellow and orange, too?
The coat my father gave to me?
    My brothers took it away, you see.

Today my brothers treat me mean,
    But God has shown me in a dream,
That though they've thrown me in this place,
    Someday they'll bow before my face!

But now I hear my brothers shout!
    They're coming near to draw me out!
They're selling me to a caravan
    To carry me off to Egypt land.

*"They stript Joseph out of his coat of many
colours: and they took him, and cast him
into a pit"* (Gen. 37:23, 24).

31

Joseph in Egypt

"And they brought Joseph into Egypt" (Gen. 37:28).

Far...far...away! Far...far...away!
  Joseph was taken far...far...away!
Sold as a slave...sold as a slave!
  But Joseph stayed faithful,
    honest and brave.

And when Pharaoh dreamed a very strange dream,
  He said, "Who can tell me what it could mean?"
When God told Joseph the meaning so true,
  Joseph told Pharaoh just what he should do.

"A famine is coming," the young Joseph said,
  "So store grain and corn! Then you'll have bread!"
The Pharaoh was pleased with Joseph's wise plan,
  And made Joseph ruler o'er all Egypt land.

And soon the time came when the clouds brought no rain.
  The corn would not grow, nor the fruit, nor the grain.
And men came to Joseph to bow at his feet,
  And he gave them food so their families could eat.

TOMMY, IT'S YOUR
BIRTHDAY TIME

"Teach us to number our days"
(Psalm 90:12).

Tommy, it's your
   birthday time,
     Let's all celebrate!
Tommy, blow your
   candles out,
     We'll all eat cake!

Tommy, count
   how old you are!
     One...two...three!
Open up your
   birthday gifts
     For all to see!

Everyone who's lived on earth,
   Was born a babe on his day of birth...
Every person...except two!
   See if you can tell me who!

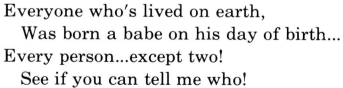

—————— and ——————
  (Adam)   (Eve)

Joseph's Hungry Brothers

"Oh, I'm hungry...Oh, so hungry!"
Joseph's older brothers said.
"Oh, I'm hungry...Oh, so hungry!
Where, oh where, can we find bread?

"Food in Egypt,
do you say?
Then let's go there
right away!"

And so they rode
o'er hill and sand,
'Till soon they came
to Egypt land.

They came before the ruler there,
And bowed before him very low.
'Twas brother Joseph whom they sold,
But this the brothers did not know.

Soon Joseph told them who he was.
He gave them bags of corn and wheat.
He said, "Now bring your families here,
So they will all have food to eat!"

The brothers pled, "Oh, do forgive us!
We're as sorry as can be!"
And Joseph said, "I do forgive you
For the wrong you did to me."

So Joseph's brothers brought their wives,
And all their sons and daughters fair,
And all the families came to live
In Egypt land with Joseph there.

*"And Joseph's ten brethren went down
to buy corn in Egypt...And Joseph said,
I am Joseph your brother whom ye sold
into Egypt" (Gen. 42:3, 45:4).*

34

Make a Brick!

"They say to us, Make brick: and thy servants are beaten" (Ex. 5:16).

Make a brick! Make a brick!
  Like a mud pie!
Lay the bricks in the sun.
  Let them all dry.

Pick up sticks! Pick up sticks!
  Gather straw all day!
Mix and mix! Mix and mix!
  Mix the straw with clay!

Don't be slow...be very quick!
  Or you'll be beaten with a stick!
Mustn't rest...mustn't play...
  The Pharaoh needs his bricks today!

What if you can't find your straw?
  That's your problem!
    HA, HA, HAW!

Hebrew children, moan and sigh!
  God in Heaven hears your cry.
Moses will be God's own man
  To lead you out from Egypt land.

"Their cry came up to God...and God heard their groaning" (Ex. 2:23, 24).

BABY MOSES

Tip..a..TEE, tip..a..TEE,
  Tip..a..TEE..a-tasket!
Hide the baby Moses
  In the little floating basket.

Float, little basket!
  Gently, gently float...
For you are baby Moses'
  Little basket boat.

Come, gentle breezes!
  Come and gently blow,
And rock the baby Moses
  Softly to and fro!

Be careful, little basket!
  Don't you tip or totter,
Or little baby Moses
  Might fall into the water!

*"She took for him an ark of bulrushes...
and she put the child therein...and she
laid it by the river's brink" (Ex. 2:3).*

36

A GOOD SISTER

When Moses' mother
had to hide him,
sister Miriam
stood beside him.
Through the river grass
she eyed him.
When he cried,
she hush-a-byed him,
till the princess
came and spied him.

Then she said,
"Oh, princess fair!
Won't the baby
lying there
need a nurse
to give him care?
To cuddle him
and comb his hair?
I can find
a nurse for you...
if, of course,
you want me to!"

Guided by
the God above her,
Miriam brought a nurse—
none other
than the baby's
own dear mother!
Wasn't she good
to her baby brother?

"Then said his sister to Pharaoh's daughter, Shall I go and call to thee a nurse? And the maid went and called the child's mother" (Ex. 2:7, 8).

37

The Happy BEARS

We never quarrel,
We never fight!
That's why we're happy,
Smiling and bright!

Why don't we quarrel?
Why don't we fight?
The Bible says
That it is not right!

"Have peace one with another" (Mark 9:50).

NOW WILL YOU LET MY PEOPLE GO?

"He turned their waters into blood...their land brought forth frogs...He smote also all the firstborn in their land" (Ps. 105: 29, 30, 36).

River is turned to bloody red.
   Every fish in the river is dead.
Water isn't fit to drink.
   All the pools and rivers stink.

Please, won't you let
  my people go?

NO, I WON'T!
NO, NO, NO!

Frogs are every...every...where!
   In your closets! In your hair!
In your ovens! In your bread!
   And when you sleep, they're in your bed!

Now, will you let
  my people go?

NO, I WON'T!
NO, NO, NO!

See the lice upon the ground!
   Gnats and lice are all around!
See the clouds of swarming flies!
   Thick as dust before your eyes!

Now, will you let
  my people go?

NO, I WON'T!
NO, NO, NO!

See the camels
  that you ride!
And every horse!
  They all have died!

Sores and boils
  on everyone!
Sores that sting
  and swell and run!

Hail is falling!
  Bing, bang, bing!
Big as rocks!
  Ping, pang, ping!

Locusts hopping
  everywhere!
Eating leaves
  till trees are bare!

Days are dark,
  as black as night!
Sun no longer
  gives its light!

Now, you'll surely
  let us go!

NO! MY ANSWER
STILL IS NO!

Came the night when no one slept.
  Mothers cried, and fathers wept.
Oldest sons were safe in bed,
  And now they find their sons are dead!
In Pharaoh's palace, too, they cried,
  For Pharaoh's oldest son has died.
"Moses! Come! My son is dead!"
  So Moses came, and Pharaoh said...

"My answer once was NO, NO, NO!
  But now I tell you, YOU MAY GO!
Take your people!
  Take your stuff!
    Get out this night!
      We've had ENOUGH!"
        And so that night
          By God's own hand,
            They all went out
              From Egypt land.

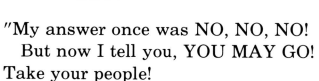

HOW DID THEY CROSS THE RED SEA?

How did they cross
to the other side?
The water was deep,
and the sea was wide.

They did not swim!
They did not wade!
They walked across
like a big parade!

God sent a wind
and it blew
and it blew,
till a pathway
appeared,
and they all
marched through!

HOORAY! HOORAY!
God made a way!
HOORAY! God saved
them all that day!

*"But the children of Israel
walked upon dry land
in the midst of the sea"*
(Ex. 14:29).

BREAD FROM HEAVEN

"Moses! Moses!"
    the angry people said,
"We're starving in this
    wilderness!
In Egypt, we had bread!

"You've brought us
    to this wilderness,
Now give us food to eat!
    Or do you want to kill us here,
And starve us with no meat?"

            "People! People!"
                Moses gently pled.
            "Listen! Listen!
                to what the Lord has said.

        "This evening you'll have flesh to eat,
            And with each morning dew,
        You'll look and find that God above
            Has rained down bread for you!"

That very night a flock of quails
    Gave meat for all the camp,
And in the early morning hours
    When all the earth was damp,
The people came from out their tents,
    So they could look around;
And everywhere was bread from heaven
    Lying on the ground!

"MANNA! MANNA!" the happy people said.
"Thank you! Thank you! Thank you, Lord, for bread!"

"Then said the Lord unto Moses, Behold, I will rain bread from heaven for you" (Ex. 16:4).

The SHOES That Never Wore Out

Have you ever had shoes
   You could wear every day,
That would stay brand new,
   And never wear away?

No, indeed you haven't!
   But listen to this news.
The children of Israel
   Had such shoes!

For forty long years
   They walked every day,
But the shoes God gave them
   Never wore away!

"And I have led you forty years in the wilderness...and thy shoe is not waxen old upon thy foot" (Deut. 29:5).

43

LAMB, LAMB!

"The lambs are for thy clothing" (Prov. 27:26).

Lamb, lamb!
  Little lamb!
Grow me wool, I pray.

I need a sweater,
    soft and warm
To keep the wind away!

SAMUEL'S COAT

Samuel! Samuel!
  Is your mother here?

      No, but she is coming!
        She comes every year.

What does she bring you?
  A bunny or a goat?

      No, my mother brings me
        A new little coat!

*"But Samuel ministered before the LORD, being a child...
Moreover his mother made him a little coat, and brought
it to him from year to year" (I Sam. 2:18, 19).*

44

THE KING IS SAD...THE KING IS MAD!

The king is sad...
  The king is mad!
Quick! Come quickly,
  shepherd lad!
Come, little David!
  Sing and play.
Cheer the king's
  sad heart today.

The king is glum...
  He's very glum!
Come, little boy,
  and strum-strum-strum!
Chase his sadness
  all away.
Strum, little boy...
  And play, play, play!

Plink-ety, plunk-ety,
  dum-dum-dum!
Play on your harp,
  a-strum-strum-strum!
Plink-ety, plunk-ety,
  ding-ding-ding!
Sing, little David!
  Sing, sing, sing!

*"David took an harp, and played
with his hand: so Saul was
refreshed, and was well"*
(I Sam. 16:23).

45

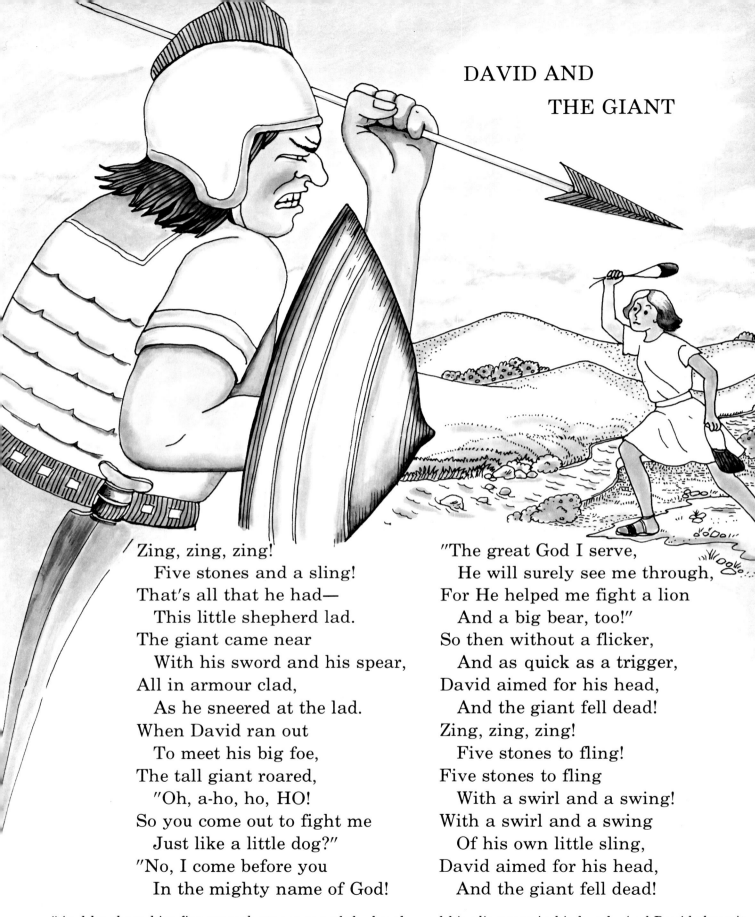

DAVID AND
THE GIANT

Zing, zing, zing!
  Five stones and a sling!
That's all that he had—
  This little shepherd lad.
The giant came near
  With his sword and his spear,
All in armour clad,
  As he sneered at the lad.
When David ran out
  To meet his big foe,
The tall giant roared,
  "Oh, a-ho, ho, HO!
So you come out to fight me
  Just like a little dog?"
"No, I come before you
  In the mighty name of God!

"The great God I serve,
  He will surely see me through,
For He helped me fight a lion
  And a big bear, too!"
So then without a flicker,
  And as quick as a trigger,
David aimed for his head,
  And the giant fell dead!
Zing, zing, zing!
  Five stones to fling!
Five stones to fling
  With a swirl and a swing!
With a swirl and a swing
  Of his own little sling,
David aimed for his head,
  And the giant fell dead!

"And he chose him five smooth stones out of the brook...and his sling was in his hand...And David slang it and smote the Philistine in his forehead...and he fell upon his face to the earth" (I Sam. 17:40, 49).

46

Elijah, Elijah!

Elijah, Elijah!
Sitting by the brook,
Look up, Elijah!
Look, look, look!

Look at the ravens
As they fly,
Bringing you your breakfast
Through the sky!

God told the ravens
To bring you bread and meat.
They've brought you your breakfast!
Now you can eat!

*"And the ravens brought him bread and flesh in the morning,
and bread and flesh in the evening; and he
drank of the brook" (I Kings 17:6).*

47

SAY YOU ARE SORRY

*"Let not the sun go down
upon your wrath"
(Eph. 4:26).*

Quick, Quick!
   The sun goeth down!
Away with your anger!
   Off with your frown!

Say you are sorry
   Before you part,
So you'll go to bed
   With a merry heart.

48

NAAMAN'S BRAND NEW SKIN

Naaman was a captain,
A captain of the king.
But Naaman didn't smile,
And Naaman didn't sing.

For Naaman was a leper
With spots upon his skin,
And nothing in the
whole wide world
could take them
off of him.

One day a little maiden—
A maiden sweet and fair—
Was helping Mrs. Naaman,
By combing out her hair.

She said to Mrs. Naaman,
"I know a godly man,
who often does
great things for God
throughout the
whole wide land."

So Naaman went to find him,
  To hear his message true,
And this is what the man of God
  Told Naaman he should do:

"Go dip down in the river,
  Exactly as I say,
And when you've dipped down seven times,
  Your spots will go away!"

So down went Captain Naaman, down to the river's shore.

He took one dip...   then two dips...   then three dips...   and then four.

He took five dips...   then six dips...   but spots still covered him,

But when he took
  the seventh dip,
  God gave him

BRAND
NEW
SKIN!

"Then went he down, and dipped himself seven times in Jordan...and his flesh came again like the flesh of a little child" (II Kings 5:14).

THE NIGHT THE LIONS
LOST THEIR APPETITE

I am a lion strong and wild,
And here is my story true.
One night as I lay in my lion's den
With other lions, too...

Right into our den
A man was thrown,
And there he stood—
One man alone.

Yes, Daniel was thrown in the midst of us,
And that could be very dangerous!
For every lion was hungry for meat,
And Daniel looked very good to eat.
And every one of us hungry beasts
Thought, "Now we'll enjoy
A pleasant feast!"

But would you believe what happened that night,
While Daniel was praying with all his might?

An angel of God
Shut our jaws so tight,
That none of us lions
Could take one bite!

No, not one bite! What a beastly shame!
For Daniel's God had made us tame!
Yes, God took away our appetite,
And Daniel was safe all through the night!

*"My God hath sent his angel,
and hath shut the lions' mouths,
that they have not hurt me"
(Dan. 6:22).*

Jonah and the BIG FISH

Preacher Jonah
　To Ninevah was sent,
To warn all the people,
　And tell them to repent.

But Jonah said, "NO!
　I won't obey!"
And he boarded a ship
　To sail the other way!

The wind came up,
　And the boat began to dip.
The sailors said,
　"Someone bad is on this ship!"

The wind grew fierce,
　And the angry waves roared,
So the sailors threw
　Jonah overboard!

Jonah cried, "HELP!"
　As he sank into the sea.
"Won't somebody please
　Come and rescue me?"

"Now the Lord had prepared a great fish to swallow up Jonah" (Jonah 1:17).

"And Jonah was in the belly of the fish three days and three nights" (Jonah 1:17).

So God took pity,
   And He answered Jonah's wish.
He was swallowed—GULP!
   By a GREAT...BIG...FISH!

When Jonah awoke
   In the belly of the whale,
He began to repent
   And to weep and to wail.

He cried out, "God,
   I will do your command!"
And the fish—in a SWISH—
   Spewed him out on dry land!

THIS BUNNY RABBIT

This bunny rabbit
went to Bible School.

This sleepy bunny
stayed home.

This bunny rabbit
learned a Bible verse.

This lazy bunny
learned none.

This bunny rabbit
had a happy time.

This grumpy bunny
was bored.

This bunny rabbit
sang a happy tune,

Singing praises
to the Lord!

"Let us go into the house of the Lord" (Ps. 122:1).

"The body is for the Lord"
(I Cor. 6:13).

THIS IS THE WAY

This is the way we wash our face.
   God wants us to be clean.
This is the way we brush our teeth
   To make them shine and gleam.

This is the way we comb our hair.
   God wants us to be neat.
This is the way we dress ourselves.
   Now don't we look real sweet!

This is the way we talk to God
   Upon our knees in prayer.
We tell Him that we love Him,
   And we thank Him
      for His care.

"Let us kneel before
* the LORD" (Ps. 95:6).*

BABY JESUS IN THE HAY

"Baaa!" said the sheep, and the cow said, "Mooo!"
    "We're glad you're here. We'll make room for you!"
The donkey awoke and went "hee-haw!"
    He said, "You can have my bed of straw!"

While Mary lay on her soft straw bed,
    A bright star shone high overhead,
And then before the break of morn,
    The Son of God Himself was born!

The doves above gave a lovely "cooo."
    The sheep said, "Baaa!" And the cow said, "Mooo!"
Where did the Baby Jesus lay?
    All snug and warm, where the cows eat hay!

"And she brought forth her firstborn son...and laid him in a manger; because there was no room for them in the inn" (Luke 2:7).

56

A BIRTHDAY GIFT FOR JESUS

My mother baked a
    gingerbread man.
She baked him just for me.
I love my little gingerbread man,
    As you can plainly see.

He's made of spicy cookie dough
    And frosting thick and sweet.
He smells so good, I lick my lips,
    For he'd be fun to eat!

He has two raisins for his eyes,
    And a raisin for his nose.
But I shall never bite his head
    Or eat his hands or toes.

What will I do with my
    gingerbread man?
    I'll hang him on our tree,
And he will be a birthday gift
    To Jesus—just from me!

*"They saw the young child with Mary, his mother...
they presented unto him gifts"* (Matt. 2:11).

THE BOY JESUS

"Jesus dear, Jesus dear!
It's time for you to rise!"
    "I am coming, mother!
    I'm opening up my eyes!"

"Jesus boy, Jesus boy!
It's time for us to pray!"
    "I will come, father!
    I'll come without delay!"

"Jesus dear, Jesus dear!
Bring me corn to grind!"
    "I will bring it, mother!
    I will quickly mind!"

"Jesus boy, Jesus boy!
Help me clean this room!"
    "Yes, I will, father!
    I'll sweep it with my broom!"

"Jesus dear, Jesus dear!
You are a special son!
Of all the children in the world—
Like you, there isn't one!"

"And he was obedient unto them" (Luke 2:51).

58

JOHN THE BAPTIST

John the Baptist lived alone
 In the desert dry and bare.
And he preached to every person
 Who came to see him there.

Do you know the kind of clothing
 John the Baptist liked to wear?
He wore a leather girdle
 And a coat of camel's hair.

Do you think he dined on baked potatoes
 And a juicy steak?
No, you'd never guess the kind of food
 That John the Baptist ate!

He caught himself big locusts
 Which were hopping everywhere,
And he finished off with honey-comb,
 Just like a hungry bear!

"And John was clothed with camel's hair...and he did eat locusts and wild honey" (Mark 1:6).

FISHERS OF MEN

Jesus, Jesus of Galilee,
Saw two men fishing
Beside the sea.
"Come!" Jesus said,
In a voice so kind.
"Leave your fish
And your nets behind.
Follow me,
And be my friend,
And I will make you
Fishers of men!"

"And Jesus, walking by the sea of Galilee, saw two brethren casting a net into the sea; for they were fishers. And he said unto them, Follow me, and I will make you fishers of men" (Matt. 4:18, 19).

JESUS LOVES
THE CHILDREN

"Dear, dear Jesus!"
The mothers softly pled,
"Bless our little children!
Lay your hands upon their head!"

Jesus told his helpers,
"Let the children come to me!"
He gathered them around Him,
And blessed them tenderly.

"And they brought young children to him, that he should touch them... and he took them up in his arms and blessed them" (Mk 10:13, 16).

60

FOOLISH MAN! WISE MAN!

There once was a foolish,
  foolish man,
Who built his house
  on a pile of sand.
The rain came down
  one stormy day,
And washed his sand pile
  all away!

With a crack-ety-crack!
  And a boom-ker-SLAM!
His house fell flat
  upon the sand!

The wise man built
  on a solid rock,
With a bang-bang-bang,
  And a knock-knock-knock!
A storm came up,
  And the rain came down,
But the wise man's house
  Stood safe and sound.

He sat in his house,
  And he smiled all day,
For he knew that his house
  Would not wash away.
And the clock on the wall
  Said, "Tick-tock-tock!
Aren't you glad you built
  On a solid rock?"

*"And the rain descended, and the floods came, and the winds blew and beat upon that house;
and it fell not: for it was founded upon a rock" (Matt. 7:25).*

Waves, Be Still!

The billowy waves were splashing and dashing!
    The wind was blowing ooh-ooh!
The men in the boat were shaking and quaking.
    They cried out, "Oh, Lord, where are you?"

The boat was tipping and dipping and flipping!
    The men were tossing around!
With trembling hearts, they shivered and quivered,
    And cried out, "We're all sure to drown!"

The Savior awoke in the boat and He spoke.

    He commanded the storm to cease.

The waves stopped their soaring, the wind stopped its roaring,

    And suddenly...all was peace!

The men were as happy as happy could be,

    For now they were safely afloat

      Upon a beautiful, peaceful sea

      In a peaceful little boat.

"And his disciples awoke him, saying, Lord, save us: we perish...Then he arose, and rebuked the winds and the sea; and there was a great calm" (Matt. 8:25, 26).

SOMEDAY I'LL LIVE
IN HEAVEN

One, two, three...
Birds live in a tree.

Three, four, five...
Bees live in a hive.

Four, five, six...
Beavers live in sticks.

Six, seven, eight...
Fish live in a lake.

Seven, eight, nine...
Squirrels live in the pine.

Nine, ten, eleven...
Someday I'll live
in Heaven!

"In my Father's house are many mansions...
I go to prepare a place for you" (Jn 14:2).

THREE SCRUBBED PIGS

Three scrubbed pigs,
  Three scrubbed pigs.
See how they shine!
  See how they shine!
The farmer washed them so very clean.
  They shimmer and sparkle
    and shine and gleam!
Did you ever see any pigs so clean
  As three scrubbed pigs!
    Three scrubbed pigs!

Three muddy pigs,
  Three muddy pigs.
No longer clean.
  No longer clean.
As soon as the farmer set them free,
They got as dirty as dirty can be.
They love to be dirty, it's easy to see.
  Three muddy pigs!
  Three muddy pigs!

"The sow that was washed is turned again to her wallowing in the mire" (II Peter 2:22).
"Create in me a clean heart" (Ps. 51:10).

THE LITTLE GIRL IS ALIVE!

The little girl is alive and well!
    Who brought her back to life?
Why, Jesus did! Of course, of course!
    For He is the Lord of life!

How did He do it? What did He say?
    He took her by the hand,
And while her parents bowed to pray,
    He issued a command:

"Get up, little girl! Rise up! Rise up!"
    And what did the little girl do?
She jumped right up—no longer dead—
    She arose and stood beside her bed!
"Now give her food to eat!" He said.
    They quickly ran
        and brought her bread.
And what did she do? She ate!
    For she was no longer dead!

No longer dead! Their joy ran wild!
    For she was alive—their only child!
So Jairus and his happy wife
    Gave thanks unto the Lord of life!

"And he took the damsel by the hand, and said unto her, Damsel, arise. And straightway the damsel arose...And he commanded that something should be given her to eat" (Mk 5:41-43).

WHEN I'M SICK

When I'm sick
  and have the flu,
Mother knows
  just what to do.
She tucks me gently
  into bed,
And lays a cloth
  upon my head.

She brings a glass
  of juice to drink,
With ice that tinkles
  "clink...clink...clink!"
And if my pillow
  has a lump,
She fluffs it 'till
  it's soft and plump.

Then she prays,
  "Dear God above,
Heal this child
  I dearly love."
And then she leaves
  me with a smile,
And says, "Now dear,
  just rest a while!"

*"I am the Lord
that healeth thee"
(Ex. 15:26).*

SUZIE AND BILLY

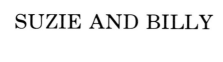

Suzie, Suzie!
  Weepy Suzie!
Why do you sit and cry?

    Billy, Billy!
      Willy-nilly!
    Poked his finger in my eye!

Suzy, Suzy,
  Smiling Suzy!
What made your crying end?

    Billy, Billy,
      Said, "I'm sorry!
    Please be my friend again!"

"And be ye kind one to another, tenderhearted, forgiving one another" (Eph. 4:32).

HE WALKED
ON THE WATER—HE DID!

When Jesus told Peter
    to walk on the water—he did!
With both eyes on Jesus,
    he walked on the water—he did!

But when he looked down
    at the boisterous waves,
He lost all his faith—it fled!
He started to sink
    in the watery deep,
And down went his feet—like lead!

But Jesus reached out
    to Peter to catch him—He did!
Yes, Jesus reached out
    to Peter to catch him—He did!

He reached out to Peter
    and gave him His hand.
Then Peter walked safely
    as though on dry land!
With Jesus beside him,
    with Jesus to guide him,
He walked on the water—he did!

"And when Peter was come down out of the ship, he walked on the water, to go to Jesus. But when he saw the wind boisterous, he was afraid, and beginning to sink, he cried, Lord, save me" (Matt. 14:29, 30).

69

THE BOY WHO SHARED HIS LUNCH

"Little boy, little boy,
  I hesitate to ask it...
Little boy, could you share
  Whatever's in your basket?"

"Take it, sir! Take it, sir!
  It's just a tiny lunch.
With all the many people here,
  It isn't very much.
There're only five small barley loaves
  And these two little fish.
My mother fixed them just for me,
  But take them if you wish!"

And as the little boy looked on,
  His eyes popped out his head!
For everyone had fish to eat,
  And everyone had bread!
For when the Savior took his lunch,
  And asked a blessing on it,
Each time a piece was broken off,
  A new one grew upon it!

Yes, everyone had lots to eat.
  Each person ate his fill.
And when they all could eat no more,
  There were twelve baskets still!

"Then he took the five loaves and the two fishes, and looking up to heaven, he blessed them, and brake...And they did eat, and were all filled; and there was taken up of fragments that remained to them twelve baskets" (Luke 9:16, 17).

70

SELFISH SUE!

Selfish Sue, selfish Sue,
   With toys of every kind!
You never share! You never share!
   You say, "They are all mine!"

Selfish Sue with face so blue,
   The Bible says, "Be kind."
Share your toys with girls and boys,
   And then your face will shine!

"Be ye kind one to another" (Eph. 4:32).

Mary and Martha

Mary, Mary!
  Why do you tarry?
Sitting at Jesus' feet?

Sister Martha's
  Out in the kitchen,
Fixing Him food to eat!

Martha, Martha!
  Why are you fretting?
Why do you speak so sharp?

Sister Mary's
  Listening to Jesus—
Listening with all her heart!

*"And she had a sister, called Mary, who
sat at Jesus' feet and heard his word.
But Martha was cumbered
about much serving, and said,
Lord, dost thou not care
that my sister hath left me
to serve alone?"
(Luke 10:39, 40).*

72

I HAVE TEN DIMES!

With one I'll buy
  A whistle to blow.
With one I'll buy
  Some seeds to grow.

With one I'll buy
  A flower for mother.
With one I'll buy
  A toy for my brother.

With one I'll buy
  A book to read.
With one I'll buy
  A pencil I need.

With one I'll buy
  A fish for my tank.
And one I'll save
  In my piggy bank.

With one I'll buy
  A brand new rule,
And one I'll take
  To Bible School...

To give to God
  Who loves me so,
And gives me
  Good things
    Here below.

*"God loveth a cheerful
giver" (II Cor. 9:7).*

73

THE LOST SHEEP

One-sheep, two-sheep,
Three-sheep, four...
Five little baa-sheep
Through the door.

Six-sheep, seven-sheep,
Eight-sheep, nine.
Ninety-nine baa-sheep,
Looking fine!

One sheep's missing!
Where can he be?
Over the hillside?
Under a tree?

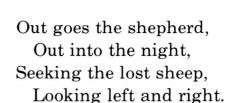

Out goes the shepherd,
Out into the night,
Seeking the lost sheep,
Looking left and right.

Out goes the shepherd,
Out into the cold,
Leaving the ninety-nine,
Safe in the fold.

"Come, little lost sheep!
Hurry to the fold!
Come, little sheep,
It's getting dark and cold!"

"Baaa!" cried the lost sheep.
The shepherd looked around,
And there he saw the lost sheep,
Lying on the ground.

"Rejoice!" cried the shepherd.
"At last my sheep is found!"

*"What man having an hundred sheep, if he lose one,
doth not leave the ninety and nine and go after
the lost until he find it? And when he hath found it,
he layeth it on his shoulders rejoicing" (Luke 15: 4, 5).*

THE DEAD MAN WHO WALKED

Come to the town of Bethany.
     Here's where Mary and Martha abide.
Let's walk down the street, and stop at their house.
     And now, let's enter and go inside.

Mary is sitting and weeping and crying.
     Lazarus, the brother she loved, has died.
Now we see that sister Martha
     Hurries to go to Mary's side.

"Mary," she whispers, "Jesus is here!
     He's coming this way, and is calling for thee.
Quick! Wipe the tears from off of your face,
     And put on your wraps and come with me."

When Mary met Jesus, she fell at his feet,
     And weeping and sobbing, she softly cried,
"Jesus, my Lord, if you'd only been here,
     I know that my brother would not have died!"

76

Jesus asked sadly, "Where have they laid him?"
"Come!" they answered. "We'll show you his grave."
And when they had come to the place where they laid him,
Jesus said, "Quick! Roll the stone from the cave!"

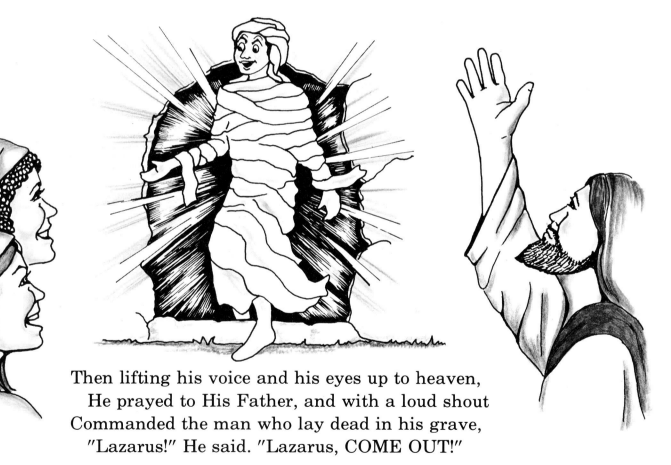

Then lifting his voice and his eyes up to heaven,
He prayed to His Father, and with a loud shout
Commanded the man who lay dead in his grave,
"Lazarus!" He said. "Lazarus, COME OUT!"

As everyone breathlessly looked toward the grave,
They gasped at a sight that no tongue could tell,
For coming right forth from the door of the cave
Walked Lazarus, the dead man, ALIVE AND WELL!

"He cried with a loud voice, Lazarus, come forth. And he that was dead came forth" (Jn 11:43, 44).

TEN SICK MEN

Ten sick men knelt by Jesus to pray,
  "Please, dear Jesus, make us well today!"
The ten sick men, Jesus healed that day,
  And ten merry men went on their merry way.

But one came back, and he knelt down to say,
  "Thank you, Jesus, for healing me today!"
But then Jesus said, "Did I not heal ten?
  Where—oh, where— are the other nine men?"

"And one of them, when he saw that he was healed, turned back...and fell down on his face at his feet, giving him thanks...And Jesus said, Were there not ten cleansed? But where are the nine? (Lk. 17:15-17).

78

I'M GOING TO BIBLE SCHOOL!

"Why are you waking so early, Ted?"
   "I'm going to Bible School!" he said.

"Why are you jumping right out of bed?"
   "I'm going to Bible School!" he said.

"Why are you brushing the hair on your head?"
   "I'm going to Bible School!" he said.

"Why are you mending your shirt with the thread?"
   "I'm going to Bible School!" he said.

"Why are you eating your berries and bread?"
   "I'm going to Bible School!" he said.

"Who will go with you, little Ted?"
   "Betty and Bobby, and Sue and Ned!

"Daddy will pull the little red sled,
   And we'll all go to Bible School!" he said.

"I was glad when they said unto me, Let us go into the house of the Lord" (Ps. 122:1).

THE BLIND MAN'S SURPRISE

"Bartimaeus, Bartimaeus!
   Is it true that you can't see us?
Can't you see my face at all?
   Can't you see the grass so tall?
Can't you see the sky so blue?
   Tell us now, can this be true?"

"I can surely tell you true,
   I can't see the sky so blue.
I can't see the grass so tall.
   I can't see your face at all.
I can hear your voice so kind.
   I can feel your hand on mine,
But I can't see you—I am blind!"

"Bartimaeus, do you hear?
  Someone's coming very near!
All are rushing out to see!
  Is it Jesus? Can it be?
Have you heard of Jesus' fame?
  He heals the sick, and heals the lame.
Right this moment, call his name!
  Perhaps for you, he'll do the same!"

Bartimaeus cried aloud,
  Shouting high above the crowd.
Jesus answered, "Come to me!
  Tell me what I can do for thee."
Bartimaeus voiced his prayer,
  As Jesus stood beside him there.
"Lord," he said, "if I could see—
  Oh, how happy I would be!"

Jesus touched the blind man's eyes.
  They opened up in wide surprise.
And Bartimaeus—all amazed—
  Just stood and gazed...and gazed...and gazed!

Then he cried in wild delight,
  "Thank you, Jesus, for my sight!
Now I see the grass so tall,
  And all the children, short and small,
And now I see the grass and skies,
  For you have opened up my eyes!"

"The blind man said, Lord, that I might receive my sight. And Jesus said, Thy faith hath made thee whole. And immediately he received his sight" (Mark 10:51, 52).

MR. ZACCHAEUS,
WHY ARE YOU SAD?

"Mr. Zacchaeus, why are you sad?"
  "If I could see Jesus, I would be glad.
But I am so small...and others so tall...
  I can't see over their heads at all!"

"Mr. Zacchaeus, stand on your toes!
  Pull on your chin, and tug on your nose!"
"No, I can't stretch enough to see,
  But I can climb up in this sycamore tree!"

"Mr. Zacchaeus, what can you see?"
  "I can see Jesus looking at me!"
"What is He doing, and what does He say?"
  "He says He is coming to my house today!"

"And he sought to see Jesus and could not, because he was little of stature. And he climbed up into a sycamore tree to see him...And Jesus said, Zacchaeus, make haste, and come down; for today I must abide at thy house" (Lk. 19:3-5).

HERE IS NED

Here is Ned—good, little Ned!
Before he eats, he bows his head,
And though he's hungry for his bread,
He takes not a bite till the blessing is said!

"Be thankful unto him" (Ps. 100:4).

LITTLE ANNIE

Little Annie Crocker
   Sat upon her rocker,
     Reading her Bible on her knee.
Along came her teacher
   With the village preacher,
     And said, "What a blessed
       girl is she!"

"From a child thou hast known the holy
*   scriptures" (II Tim. 3:15).*

GOOD MORNING, LITTLE DONKEY!

Good morning, little donkey!
Stop your eating hay!
Jesus has need of you
To carry Him today!

Smile, little donkey!
Lift your ears and bray,
For you're a special donkey
Chosen for this day.

Be careful, little donkey!
Don't you trip or sway,
But carry the Lord Jesus
Gently on His way.

Be careful, little donkey!
Watch your little feet!
Don't stumble on the branches
Scattered on the street.

Listen, little donkey!
Hear the children sing!
They're singing loud hosannas
To Jesus Christ, the King!

"They found the colt tied by the door...and they brought the colt to Jesus, and he sat upon him. And many spread their garments in the way: and others cut down branches off the trees...and cried, saying, Hosanna; Blessed is he that cometh in the name of the Lord" (Mk. 11:4, 7-9).

WHAT CAN I DO FOR YOU?

Father, what can I do for you
  To show you love today?
I'll bring you frosty lemonade
  With cookies on a tray!

Mother, what can I do for you
  To show how dear you are?
I'll bring you yellow daffodils
  And put them in a jar!

"Honour thy father and mother"
(Eph. 6:2).

THE FIRST GLAD EASTER

"Crucify Him! Let Him die!"
　Said the angry throng.
And so they took our Jesus,
　Who never did a wrong...

And nailed Him to a wooden cross
　To let him bleed and die,
While Mary, his dear mother,
　And friends stood sadly by.

They placed an ugly crown of thorns
　Upon his blessed head.
Soldiers pierced Him with a spear.
　They said, "This man is dead!"

Loving friends with hands so kind,
　Laid Him gently in a grave.
Soldiers rolled a heavy stone
　O'er the doorway of the cave.

An angel rolled the stone away
　On that first glad Easter Day!
"He's not here!" the angel said,
　"Christ is risen from the dead!"

"He is not here, but is risen" (Luke 24:6).

86

NOW I LAY ME

Now I lay me down to sleep.
  I pray the Lord my soul to keep
Through the darkness of the night,
  Till I wake in sunlight bright.

"I will lay me down in peace, and sleep: for thou, LORD, makest me dwell in safety" (Ps. 4:8).

DOUBTING THOMAS

"But Thomas was not with them when Jesus came. The other disciples therefore said unto him, We have seen the Lord. But he said, Except I shall see in his hands the print of the nails...I will not believe" (John 20:24, 25).

"Thomas, Thomas!
While you were out,
Jesus came—without a doubt!"

"Jesus came while I was out?
That I really, truly doubt!"

"Thomas, Thomas,
Why are you pouting?"

"Why am I pouting?
Because I am doubting!
Why do I doubt?
Because I was out!
And that's what my doubt
Is all about!"

"Thomas, Thomas...here I am!
Listen now to my command!
Touch my wounds with your own hand.
Then you'll believe and understand!"

"Jesus, Jesus!
Now I see!
You are the One
Who died for me!
You have risen
From the dead!
You are alive—
Just like they said!
Now their words
I do receive.
Now that I see you—
I BELIEVE!"

I HAVE A PILLOW

I have a pillow
    And I have a bed.
I have a soft place
    Where I lay my head.

The fox has its hole,
    The bird has its nest.
God gives to everyone
    A soft place to rest.

"The foxes have holes, and the birds of the air have nests" (Matt. 8:20).

89

A LITTLE GIRL'S DREAM

A little girl dreamed a dream one night
    That the animals told her how to do right.
Listen now, and see if you
    Can guess who told her what to do!

"Always wear a great big smile,"
    Said a big-mouthed ——————————.
                       (crocodile)

"Go to bed by eight or nine!"
    Said a sleepy ——————————.
               (porcupine)

"Never frown, and never scowl!"
    Said a quiet, wise old ——————.
                   (owl)

"Show your neighbors lots of love,"
    Cooed a lovely, pure-white ——————.
                   (dove)

"Keep your words as sweet as honey,"
Said a bright-eyed little —————.
(bunny)

"Don't be sour. Enjoy a laugh!"
Said the jolly tall —————————.
(giraffe)

"Be a helpful little girl,"
Said a frisky, little ——————————.
(squirrel)

"Always do the things that please,"
Buzzed a pair of honey ————.
(bees)

The animals gave her good advice
On how to be happy, how to be nice.
But the best advice that's ever heard
Is what God tells us in His Word!

"DO UNTO OTHERS AS YOU WOULD HAVE THEM DO UNTO YOU."
Luke 6:31

"LOVE ONE ANOTHER."
Jn 15:12

"BE YE KIND."
Eph. 4:32

JIMMY'S PRAYER

Jimmy was a teaser.
  He played a little game.
He yelled and told his mother
  That the kitchen was aflame.

She ran into the kitchen,
  And her heart was pounding wild.
But when she saw it wasn't true,
  She said, "Oh, dearest child...

"Jesus wants us to be true
  In every word we say,
And never, never tell a lie—
  Not even just in play!"

When Jimmy's mother told him this,
  He quickly bowed his head,
And prayed, "Dear Lord, forgive me
  For the untrue words I said.

"And help me, please, from day to day
  The truth to always speak."
Then Jimmy's mother hugged him close
  And kissed him on the cheek.

"For my mouth shall speak truth" (Prov. 8:7).

"And they shall see the Son of man coming in the clouds" *(Matt. 24:30).*

WHENEVER I SEE A CLOUD

Whenever I see a cloud, I say,
"Is Jesus coming to earth today?"
A cloud took Jesus up and away.
A cloud will bring Him back someday!

JESUS LOVES ME

Jesus loves me, this I know,
  For my grandma tells me so.
When she holds me on her knee,
  She reads Bible stories to me.
I love Jesus—yes, I do!
  And my grandma loves Him, too!

"We love him because he first loved us" *(I Jn 4:19).*

THE END

Dear little friend
  You've come to the end,
But you may read me
  Again and again.
Then you'll remember
  Each story true
From God's Holy Word
  That we've shared
    with you.

"I will not forget thy Word" (Psalm 119:16).

"Feed my lambs" (John 21:15).